THE ULTIMATE GUIDE

everything men can say to women without offending them

A. Pauline Lyre